DEVELOPING LI

**Photocopiable
teaching resources
for literacy**

SENTENCE STRUCTURE AND PUNCTUATION

Ages 4–5

Christine Moorcroft

A & C Black • London

Contents

Published 2007 by A & C Black Publishers Limited
38 Soho Square, London W1D 3HB
www.acblack.com

ISBN 978–0-7136-8435-3

Copyright text © Christine Moorcroft 2007
Copyright illustrations © Nick Flint 2007
Copyright cover illustration © Jan McCafferty 2007
Editor: Clare Robertson
Designed by HL Studios, Oxford

The authors and publishers would like to thank Ray Barker and
Fleur Lawrence for their advice in producing this series of books.

A CIP catalogue record for this book is available from the British Library.

Printed and bound in Great Britain by Martins the Printers, Berwick-on-Tweed.

A & C Black uses paper produced with elemental chlorine-free pulp, harvested from managed sustainable forests.

Introduction

100% New Developing Literacy: Sentence Structure and Punctuation is a series of seven photocopiable activity books for developing children's understanding of sentences and their ability to form simple sentences.

The books provide learning activities to support strand 11 (Sentence structure and punctuation) of the literacy objectives of the Primary Framework for Literacy and Mathematics and of the Early Learning Goals for the Foundation Stage. Children learn to write their own names and other things such as labels and captions, and begin to form simple sentences sometimes using punctuation.

Some of activities are designed to be carried out with the whole class, some with small groups and some individually. Some of them are intended for teachers to read aloud to the children and to invite their responses; some are presented in the form of games and other activities or for oral responses; others require a written response. They can be used for different purposes: to introduce activities in various contexts, to support activities or to help with the assessment of children's progress.

Reading

Most children will be able to carry out the activities independently. It is not expected that they should be able to read all the instructions on the sheets, but that someone will read them to or with them. The children gradually become accustomed to seeing instructions, and learn their purpose long before they can read them.

Organisation

The activities require very few resources besides pencils, crayons, scissors, glue and word-banks. Other materials are specified in the Teachers' notes on the pages: for example, information books and simple picture dictionaries.

Extension activities

Most of the activity sheets end with a challenge (*Now try this!*) which reinforces and extends the children's learning and provides the teacher with an opportunity for assessment. These more challenging activities might be appropriate for only a few children; it is not expected that the whole class should complete them. On some pages there is space for the children to complete the extension activities, but others will require a notebook or a separate sheet of paper.

Accompanying CD

The enclosed CD-ROM contains electronic versions of a the activity sheets in the book for printing, editing, savin or display on an interactive whiteboard. Our uniqu browser-based interface makes it easy to select page and to modify them to suit individual pupils' needs. Se page 10 for further details.

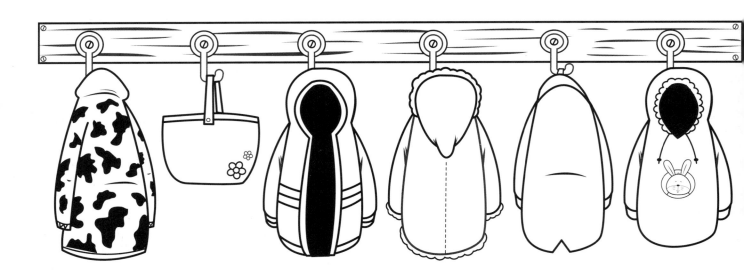

Notes on the activities

The notes below expand upon those which are provided at the bottom of most activity pages. They give ideas and suggestions for making the most of the activity sheet, including suggestions for the whole-class introduction, the plenary session or follow-up work using an adapted version of the activity sheet. To help teachers to select appropriate learning experiences for their pupils, the activities are grouped into sections within each book, but the pages need not be presented in the order in which they appear, unless otherwise stated.

Labels and signs

The activities in this section focus on the reading and writing of simple labels, including words for names, places and objects. They provide opportunities for reading and writing labels and develop skills in using word-banks for a purpose. The children are also encouraged to use their phonic knowledge to support reading and writing. Labels are not written in sentences and prepare for later work in which the children learn about sentences; they can be used as a contrast for demonstrating the difference between a sentence and a word.

Crazy cloakroom (page 11) provides practice in reading names in meaningful contexts. It is useful if the children first have practice in finding one another's names around the classroom: for example, on cloakroom hooks and lunchboxes and on name cards used for activities such as registration.

My book (page 12) is about writing the children's names in a sentence. They practise writing their own names and those of others in a meaningful context. The children could write their names on ready-made bookplates or they could design their own. These could be scanned and duplicated for them to label some of their books.

Pets' corner (page 13) develops an understanding of how labels can be used for giving information and provides practice in using word-banks. It could be used to support work on animals in knowledge and understanding of the world (science). The children could collect and label pictures of pets (their own pets, where possible) for a pets' display or models of pets for a three-dimensional model of a 'pets' corner'.

This way (page 14) develops an understanding of how signs can be used for giving information. It could be used to support work in knowledge and understanding of the world (geography). The children could make a collage of the local area and make signs with which to indicate the locations of features. They could also make signs for the classroom or school to help visitors to find their way around.

All wrong! (page 15) develops skills in reading and understanding text in the environment and how signs can be used for giving information, and provides practice in using word-banks. Encourage the children to notice signs which help them to find their way around buildings or to know how to use places: for example, 'entrance', 'exit', 'in', 'out', 'open', 'closed', 'ladies', 'gents', 'private'.

Lists

The activities in this section are about making and using lists. They focus on the format of lists and how this suits their purpose. The children develop an understanding of an everyday use of writing. These simple signs are not written in sentences and prepare for later work in which the children learn about sentences; they can be used as a contrast for demonstrating the difference between a sentence and a group of words which is not a sentence.

Cinderella's shopping list (page 16) uses a familiar story to develop children's understanding of an everyday use of text. They should first have read or listened to the story of Cinderella and focused on the part where the fairy godmother sends Cinderella to find a series of items for use in her magic spells. (A pumpkin for the coach, mice for the horses, lizards for the coachmen, rats for the footmen.)

My day (page 17) provides an opportunity for the children to develop an understanding of an everyday use of text. This could be used to support the setting of targets during a morning or afternoon. The children could read their list to a partner, who could help them to check each item and tick it when they complete it. (You could add 'tick boxes' for this.)

Teddy bears' picnic (page 18) encourages the children to think about planning and to use their developing writing skills to help them in this, and provides practice in using word-banks. It could be used to support work on healthy eating in personal and social development and citizenship. The children could also write menus for school meals or for a class café, which could also be linked with work in mathematics.

Little Red Riding Hood's basket (page 19) requires the children to read labels (supported by pictures) in order to find out information. They use labels to find out about the contents of Little Red Riding Hood's basket. In the extension activity they write their own lists. This could be linked with work in mathematics – they could write shopping lists and include the prices of the items. They could also write shopping lists for making a picnic (link this with page 16) or they could plan shopping lists for other story characters.

The direction of text

These activities develop the children's understanding that text is written from left to right across a page.

Place to place (page 20) focuses on the direction of text from left to right. Encourage the children to walk their fingers along the footsteps as they read each word, emphasising where the sentence starts and the direction in which they read it. You could also chalk sentences on giant footprints in the playground (from left to right) and help the children to read them as they follow the trail.

Where did they go? (page 21) focuses on the direction of text from left to right. After the children have completed the sentences, encourage them to slide a finger along the arrow as they read each word, emphasising where the sentence starts and the direction in which they read it. You could also chalk giant arrows in the playground (from left to right), write sentences along them and help the children to read them as they follow the trail.

Travel tales (page 22) focuses on the direction of text from left to right. After the children have completed the sentences, encourage them to move a finger along the vans, boats and sheep as they read each word, emphasising where the sentence starts and the direction in which they read it.

Messages

This set of activities focuses on the use of greetings and communicating short pieces of information in messages.

Birthday card (page 23) provides practice in writing greetings for a familiar occasion. The children write a familiar phrase, and inside the card they write familiar greetings for a birthday. Encourage them to use the *Greetings word-bank* on page 26. Some children could word-process the greeting, print it and glue it onto the birthday card. They could make birthday cards for one another, for their families and for friends of the school.

Get well soon (page 24) provides practice in writing greetings for a familiar occasion. The children write a familiar phrase, and inside the card they write a familiar short sentence for sending good wishes to someone who is ill. Encourage them to use the *Greetings word-bank* on page 28. Some children could word-process the greeting, print it and glue it onto the get well card. This page will be useful on occasions when a member of the school or a friend of the school is ill and could be incorporated into work in personal and social development and citizenship.

Teddy's party (page 25) focuses on the use of a sentence which communicates information in a familiar context. The children could bring in party invitations they have received (or you could bring in some ready-prepared invitations for them to read). Help them to read the information on the invitations and ask them whose party they are for, on what day or date, at what time and where. Point out how the sentence is set out in order to make this information clear (the sentence is not written all on one line).

Don't forget! (page 26) focuses on the use of writing for an everyday purpose – to remind others or oneself to do something. It provides reminders written in the form of simple sentences (and in the imperative form, although this may not be discussed with the children). To prepare for this activity the children (with permission) could bring in a message from a memory board at home, if they have one. Help them to read the messages and discuss their purposes. Point out any sentences.

Dear Humpty Dumpty (page 27) provides an opportunity to write sentences for a purpose and to use a word-bank to support the children's writing. This could be linked with work in citizenship and speaking and listening, in which the children could discuss safe and unsafe places to play. Their message could be to tell Humpty Dumpty how to stay safe. Read their letters with them and focus on making sense of their sentences.

Greetings word-bank (page 28) supports any writing of greetings and messages. It could be copied and laminated for each group to refer to when writing these.

Missing words

These activities develop the children's understanding of how sentences make sense by omitting vital words, which they are required to insert. Go through the activities with the children, using an interactive whiteboard, before they try them for themselves.

Balloons (page 29) helps the children to understand that a sentence should make sense. To prepare for this you could write very short, simple sentences on large cards and provide missing words on card strips. The children could try different words in the gaps to find out which make sense. Encourage them to read the sentences they have made aloud to check them. They could do this with a partner.

The bee (page 30) is about recognising when a group of words makes sense as a sentence and when it does not. The children look at a labelled diagram in order to find the missing words with which to complete sentences. This could be linked with work in knowledge and understanding of the world (science) on living things. The children could learn how to identify bees and find out about them (and the different parts of their body) from books and posters. The extension activity encourages them to make up their own sentences about bees. You could adapt this to develop sentence work on other animals the children observe. It could be linked with work on mathematics, for example: making up sentences about the numbers of different body parts animals have.

Sentence flowers (page 31) is about recognising when a group of words makes sense as a sentence and when it does not. The children read a set of missing words from which to choose one to complete sentences. This could be linked with work in knowledge and understanding of the world (science) on living things. The children could learn how to identify

different flowers and find out about them (and the names of different parts of them) from books and posters. The extension activity encourages them to make up their own sentences about flowers. You could adapt this to develop sentence work on flowers the children observe.

Capital letters

These activities focus on simple uses of capital letters to begin words and sentences: for names, the personal pronoun 'I' and for starting a sentence. It is useful to provide, for reference, an alphabet strip or chart showing the upper- and lower-case letters of the alphabet. Most software for interactive whiteboards includes alphabets for use on screen.

Names (page 32) draws attention to the use of initial capital letters for names. The children could first find words which begin with the same letters as their names and compare the initial letters when written. Draw out that their names begin with capital letters.

Name that dog (page 33) is about using capital letters to begin names – including the names given to animals. The children could first find out at home how to write the names of their pets or those of their friends, relations or neighbours. After completing this page they could draw feeding bowls for other dogs or cats they know and add their names.

Capital I (page 34) focuses on the personal pronoun 'I' and the use of a capital I for writing it. The children could first be encouraged to say something about themselves. Draw out their use of 'I' and ask them who 'I' means. Ask them if it means the same if you say it or if someone else says it.

I see (page 35) focuses on the use of the personal pronoun 'I' instead of a person's name when the person is talking about himself or herself. It also reinforces the use of a capital I for writing it. The children could use a chalk board or word processor to write sentences beginning with their name and then rub out or delete their name and replace it with 'I'.

Starting off and **Start with a capital** (pages 36–37) focus on the use of a capital letter to start a sentence. The children could also look for capital letters in books they read individually or during shared or guided reading sessions. It is also useful to provide upper- and lower-case wooden or plastic letters with which they can make up words and sentences.

Full stops

These activities develop the children's understanding of the full stop and what a sentence is.

A full stop and **Stop it!** (pages 38–39) are about the use of a full stop to end a sentence. The children could first practise making full stops on chalk boards and on large sheets of paper in different media. They could look for the full stop on a keyboard and on the punctuation screen of a mobile phone.

Full stop finder: 1 and **2** (pages 40–41) develop the children's understanding that a sentence is not the same as a line of text and that a full stop ends a sentence and not a line of text. They could also find the full stops at the ends of sentences in books they read, particularly those in which sentences extend over more than one line.

Mixed-up sentences

These activities develop the children's awareness of the meaning of a sentence. They contain words they will have come across during work across the curriculum, and many words they can read by using their developing understanding and skills in phonics.

At the seaside: 1 and **2** (pages 42–43) provide sequences of words which most children will be able to read, but which do not make sense in that order. Cutting out the individual words helps the children to distinguish between a word and a sentence and through rearranging the words the children develop an awareness that a sentence should make sense. During work in other subjects, particularly knowledge and understanding of the world, the children could be given mixed-up sentences and asked to arrange them to make a sentence.

Leap frogs (page 44) is more challenging than pages 42–43 in that the children are asked to rearrange a set of words to make sense without cutting them out.

Word birds and **Robots** (pages 45–46) are more challenging than page 44 in that the children are asked to use word-banks as the starting point for making sentences. In work in other subjects they could be provided with word-banks containing all the words they need to write a sentence, but not in the order in which they will write them. It is useful to follow the convention of alphabetical order for word-banks to prepare for the use of simple dictionaries.

Sentence-building

These activities develop the children's awareness of the meaning of a sentence by asking them to predict a missing word, select an ending for a sentence or make up sentences from sets of words.

What did they do? (page 47) focuses on verbs, although this term is not yet introduced to the children. It emphasises that a sentence says what happens or exists. This understanding can be reinforced when the children tell or write stories. An adult acting as scribe could ask the children questions about what they did and write the answers, omitting the verb, asking the children to read the sentence to check that it is correct. The children can then identify the missing word.

The big dog (page 48) focuses on making sense of sentences through matching them to pictures and predicting the endings. Through this activity the children develop an awareness that sentences are about things which happen or exist. To prepare for it, the children could play a game in which they take turns to say what an animal or other character did, where, when or how. This could be linked with story-telling.

Sentence factory (page 49) develops skills in writing short, simple sentences. You could also make 'lift-the flap' sentence boards for the children to use in creating sentences.

Silly sentences (page 50) provides a game in which the children can use and develop their understanding of sentences. Draw out that the words of a sentence must make sense but that it can be about something silly. As an extension activity you could ask the children questions which lead to the formation of sentences: for example, 'Who?', 'What did he/she/it do?', 'Where?' (or 'When?' or 'How?'). This can be varied so that on some occasions the sentences can be silly but on others they must be sensible.

Captions

This section focuses on longer captions (captions which consist of a sentence rather than a word or phrase). The activities support non-fiction writing for work on knowledge and understanding of the world, in which the children draw pictures or take photographs of places, objects, animals or plants and then write captions giving information about them.

The park and **Zoo time** (pages 51–52) focus on writing the ending of a sentence and then using the first completed sentence as a model for others. It is useful to point out the capital letters and full stops. As a further extension activity some children could be asked to write sentences which begin 'I cannot see …' or 'At the zoo there is no …'.

In the street and **On the beach** (pages 53–54) focus on writing a word in the middle of a sentence and then using the completed sentence as a model for writing others. This format could be used for writing about a place the children visit.

Sequencing

These activities introduce the connective word 'then' and develop the children's awareness of the purpose of different words in a sentence: for example, to link it to another sentence.

Treasure hunt and **Follow my leader** (pages 55–56) introduce the use of 'then' to start a sentence and develop the children's understanding of the purpose of this word. Before beginning *Treasure Hunt* they could follow a treasure trail around the classroom or playground and say what they found. The trail could be prepared beforehand, with arrow signs to guide the children. To prepare for *Follow my leader*, you could play the game, 'Follow my leader', with the children not only copying the leader's actions, but also saying what they are doing. Afterwards ask them what they did; after the first response they should respond with sentences beginning with 'Then'.

Route cards: 1 and **2** (pages 57–58) provide routes for the children to talk about using the word 'then' where appropriate, and a format to help them to write sentences about the routes. To support work in knowledge and understanding of the world (geography) the children could make route cards, with labels, to indicate a route they have actually walked. They could talk about their routes, using sentences in the format of those on pages 53–54, and then write their sentences.

Along the street: 1 and **2** (pages 59–60) together form a game the children can play which leads to the writing of sentences beginning with 'Then'. They can look at the game board to help them to remember the sequence of the objects they saw. You could help the children to make a large floor mat in the form of the game board on which to record a real walk by drawing pictures in the correct order. They could then say and write sentences about their walk, using the floor mat (which could be covered with protective film) as a prompt. This could also be made available for free play activities.

Using rhymes, jingles and songs

These activities provide ideas for using songs, rhymes and jingles as starting points for sentence-building, including encouraging the children to make up their own songs consisting of simple sentences.

I can tap, tap, tap (page 61) provides the starting point for an action song the children can make up. It develops their ability to form sentences. In the extension activity they can add actions such as 'bang', 'hum', 'kick', 'shake' and 'wobble'. They could sing the song so that the verses are incremental, which will require them to remember all the preceding actions.

Old Macdonald's farm (page 62) develops the children's ability to make up sentences containing the connective word 'and'. They might find this difficult if they had to write the entire sentence, but here they are required only to fill one or two gaps with words provided on the page. This could be linked with work in knowledge and understanding of the world (science and geography) involving a farm visit. An activity area could be set up containing a 'farm' with model animals, tractors, people and so on.

Mrs Snip (page 63) helps the children to write sentences. They could first sing the song while performing the actions. In the extension activity they could add actions such as 'dye', 'shampoo', 'trim', 'curl', 'straighten', 'crimp'. This could be used to support work in a class 'hairdresser's corner' for role-play, which could be linked with mathematics (writing prices and bills).

Goldilocks (page 64) provides formats to help the children to write sentences about a character in a well-known story. They develop skills in considering the meaning of a sentence by predicting the missing words. They can then use the completed sentences as models for writing their own. You could provide similar sets of skeleton sentences about other stories they know.

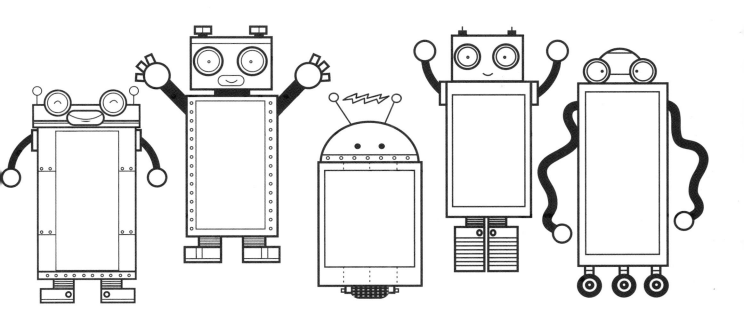

Using the CD-ROM

The PC CD-ROM included with this book contains an easy-to-use software program that allows you to print out pages from the book, to view them (e.g. on an interactive whiteboard) or to customise the activities to suit the needs of your pupils.

Getting started

It's easy to run the software. Simply insert the CD-ROM into your CD drive and the disk should autorun and launch the interface in your web browser.

If the disk does not autorun, open 'My Computer' and select the CD drive, then open the file 'start.html'.

Please note: this CD-ROM is designed for use on a PC. It will also run on most Apple Macintosh computers in Safari however, due to the differences between Mac and PC fonts, you may experience some unavoidable variations in the typography and page layouts of the activity sheets.

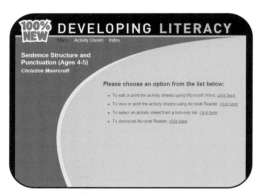

The Menu screen

Four options are available to you from the main menu screen.

The first option takes you to the Activity Sheets screen, where you can choose an activity sheet to edit or print out using Microsoft Word.

(If you do not have the Microsoft Office suite, you might like to consider using OpenOffice instead. This is a multi-platform and multi-lingual office suite, and an 'open-source' project. It is compatible with all other major office suites, and the product is free to download, use and distribute. The homepage for OpenOffice on the Internet is: www.openoffice.org.)

The second option on the main menu screen opens a PDF file of the entire book using Adobe Reader (see below). This format is ideal for printing out copies of the activity sheets or for displaying them, for example on an interactive whiteboard.

The third option allows you to choose a page to edit from a text-only list of the activity sheets, as an alternative to the graphical interface on the Activity Sheets screen.

Adobe Reader is free to download and to use. If it is not already installed on your computer, the fourth link takes you to the download page on the Adobe website.

You can also navigate directly to any of the three screens at any time by using the tabs at the top.

The Activity Sheets screen

This screen shows thumbnails of all the activity sheets in the book. Rolling the mouse over a thumbnail highlights the page number and also brings up a preview image of the page.

Click on the thumbnail to open a version of the page in Microsoft Word (or an equivalent software program, see above.) The full range of editing tools are available to you here to customise the page to suit the needs of your particular pupils. You can print out copies of the page or save a copy of your edited version onto your computer.

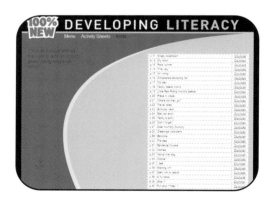

The Index screen

This is a text-only version of the Activity Sheets screen described above. Choose an activity sheet and click on the 'download' link to open a version of the page in Microsoft Word to edit or print out.

Technical support

If you have any questions regarding the *100% New Developing Literacy* or *Developing Mathematics* software please email us at the address below. We will get back to you as quickly as possible.

educationalsales@acblack.com

Crazy cloakroom

Help the children to find their coats and bags.

Tom	May	Ben	Bav	Zul	Ann

Zul

Ann

Tom

May

Ben

Bav

NOW TRY THIS!

• **Write your name on the label.**

eachers' note Ask the children to look for a name label in their coat or other garment. They could
ead one another's name labels and then hang them in the correct places by matching the name
bels. Ask them what the picture shows and how the children can find their coats. Point out how
he example has been completed and ask them to draw lines to join the children to   their coats.

**100% New Developing Literacy
Sentence Structure and
Punctuation: Ages 4–5
© A & C BLACK**

11

• Write the children's names on their bookplates.

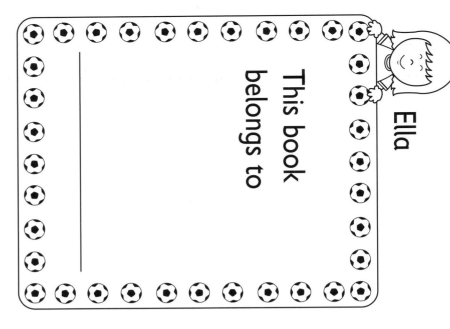

Ella

This book
belongs to

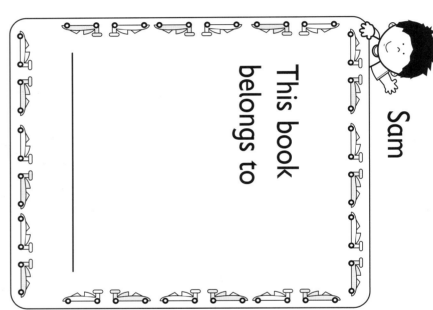

Sam

This book
belongs to

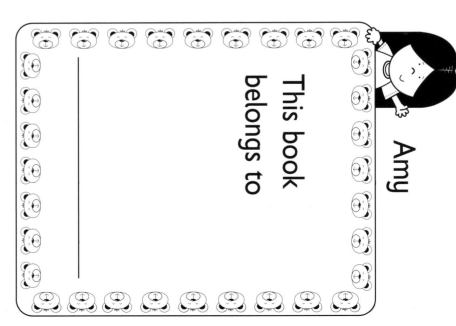

Amy

This book
belongs to

NOW TRY THIS!

• Make a bookplate for a friend.

Teachers' note Show the children a book in which a bookplate has been fixed to show whom it belongs to. Read the bookplate with them, pointing to each word. Select individual words and ask, 'What does this word say?' Then tell the children that all the words together make up a sentence. They can then complete the bookplates. Ask them to read each sentence.

100% New Developing Literacy
Sentence Structure and
Punctuation: Ages 4–5
© A & C BLACK

Pets' corner

Write the words on the signs.

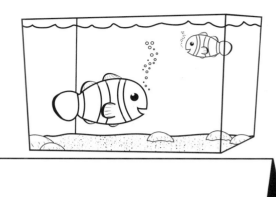

Word-bank

 cat dog   fish parrot

NOW TRY THIS!

- **Draw another pet.**
- **Write a sign.**

Use word-banks.

Teachers' note Ask the children to name the animals in the pictures and discuss what signs are used for (to tell people about something: for example, the type of animal they see in a zoo or pets' corner). Point out the word-bank and explain what it is for. Draw attention to the fact that these are *words*. The children can then copy the correct word onto each sign.

**100% New Developing Literacy
Sentence Structure and
Punctuation: Ages 4–5**
© A & C BLACK

This way

- **Write the words on the signs.**

Word-bank

beach

park

shops

woods

NOW TRY THIS!

- **Write a sign for a place you know.**

Teachers' note Remind the children of the signs they wrote for the animals in *Pets' corner* and discuss other uses of signs: for example, to tell people the way to places. Ask the children to read the words in the word-bank and ask them to match them to the pictures beside the signs. Emphasise that these are *words*. They should then be able to copy the correct word onto each sign.

100% New Developing Literacy
Sentence Structure and
Punctuation: Ages 4–5
© A & C BLACK

All wrong!

The signs are wrong.
Cross out the wrong signs.
Write the correct words.

Word-bank

down

pull

push

up

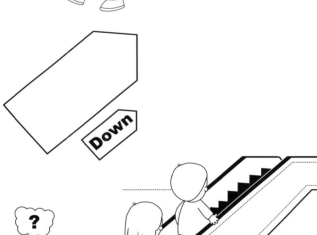

NOW TRY THIS!

• Make a sign to help
visitors at your school.

Use
word-banks.

Teachers' note Remind the children of the signs they wrote for the animals in *Pets' corner* and *This way* and discuss other uses of signs: for example, to help people to use things. Ask the children to read the words on the signs and to look at the pictures. Ask them what they *should* say. Can they find the correct *words* in the word-bank? They can then copy the correct word onto each sign.

**100% New Developing Literacy
Sentence Structure and
Punctuation: Ages 4–5**
© A & C BLACK

Cinderella's shopping list

What does Cinderella need?

- **Write four things on the shopping list.**

Shopping list

one _____

one _____

six _____

six _____

Word-bank

lizards   pumpkin

mice   rat

NOW TRY THIS!

- **Write a shopping list for another story character.**

Use word-banks.

Teachers' note Reread the part of *Cinderella* where the fairy godmother sends Cinderella to find objects she can turn into a coach, horses, driver and footmen. Discuss how Cinderella will remember what she has to find, and introduce the idea of a shopping list. Help the children to read the words in the word-bank. They should then be able to complete the list.

100% New Developing Literacy
Sentence Structure and
Punctuation: Ages 4–5
© A & C BLACK

My day

List the things you will do today.

Date: _____

Morning

Afternoon

NOW TRY THIS!

• **Write a 'things to do' list for a story character.**

Use a word-bank.

Teachers' note Remind the children that people write lists to help them to remember things. Discuss the different things the children do each day, and ask them how they remember to do them. Draw attention to any lists used in the classroom. This list format can be used to help the children to list daily tasks. They could use word-banks to help them to complete it.

100% New Developing Literacy
Sentence Structure and
Punctuation: Ages 4–5
© A & C BLACK

Teddy bears' picnic

- **Choose the picnic menu for today.**
- **Write the menu.**

Teddy bears' picnic menu

sandwiches

_____

fruit

_____

drink

_____

Word-bank   apple   egg   orange

banana   juice   tuna

cheese   milk   water

NOW TRY THIS!

- **Draw and write a picnic menu for you.**

Teachers' note It is useful if the children have first sung the song *Teddy Bears' Picnic*. Also show them some simple menus, preferably illustrated, and discuss what a menu is for. Help them to read the words in the word-bank and ask them to choose some foods for the teddy bears.

100% New Developing Literacy Sentence Structure and Punctuation: Ages 4–5
© A & C BLACK

What is in Little Red Riding Hood's basket?

Write a list.

Little Red Riding
Hood's basket

_____

_____

_____

_____

_____

Grandma's House

flowers

bread

cat

book

grapes

NOW TRY THIS!

What would you take for Grandma?

- **Write a list.**
- **Draw your basket.**

Teachers' note The children should first have read or listened to the story of _Little Red Riding Hood_. Remind them of their previous learning about shopping lists before they look at Little Red Riding Hood's basket and take turns to identify something in it. They can then list these on the shopping list. Emphasise that they have written _words_.

100% New Developing Literacy Sentence Structure and Punctuation: Ages 4–5 © A & C BLACK

Place to place

- **Read the words on the footprints.**
- **Write the sentences.**
- **Read the sentences.**

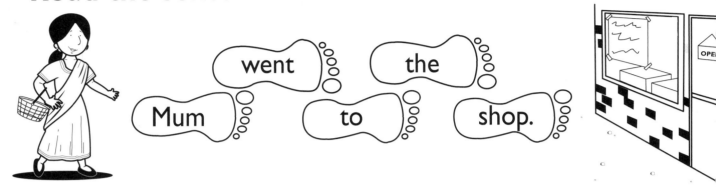

Mum went to the shop.

_____

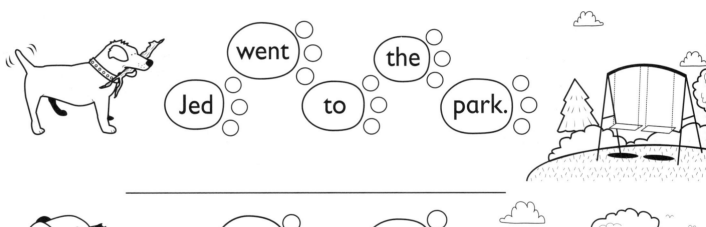

Jed went to the park.

_____

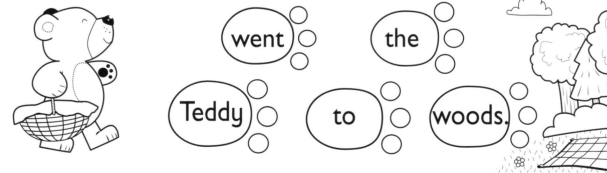

Teddy went to the woods.

_____

NOW TRY THIS!

- **Draw someone's footprints. Where did they go?**
- **Write a sentence.**

Use word-banks.

Teachers' note Ask the children to follow the footprints with a finger as you read the first sentence with them. Ask them to point to, and read, each word separately. Then ask them to reread the sentence. Draw out that the words make sense when they are put together like this; they make up a sentence. Also emphasise the direction of the forder in which the words are read.

100% New Developing Literacy
Sentence Structure and
Punctuation: Ages 4–5
© A & C BLACK

Where did they go?

Where did they go?

Follow the arrows.

Write the sentences.

Read the sentences.

The spider went to the _____ .

The owl _____ .

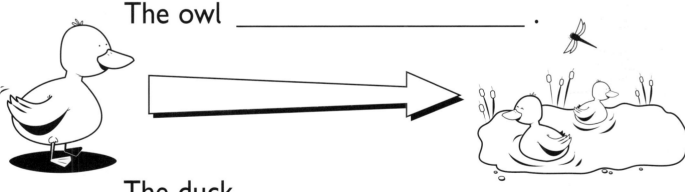

The duck _____ .

NOW TRY THIS!

Where did a story character go?

• Write a sentence about it.

Use word-banks.

Teachers' note Ask the children to follow the arrow with a finger as you read the first sentence with them. Ask them to point to, and read, each word separately. Then ask them to reread the sentence. Draw out that the words make sense when they are put together like this; they make up a *sentence*. Also emphasise the direction of the order in which the words are read.

**100% New Developing Literacy
Sentence Structure and
Punctuation: Ages 4–5**
© A & C BLACK

Travel tales

- Write the missing words.
- Write the sentences.

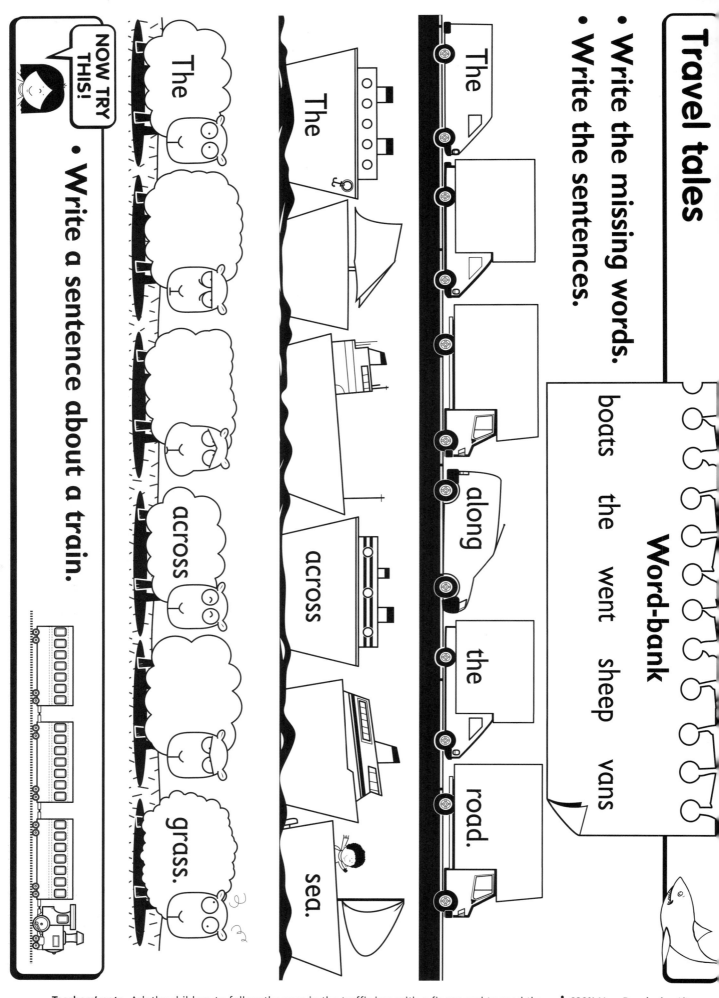

Word-bank

boats the went sheep vans

The _____ along the road.

The _____ across _____ sea.

The _____ across _____ grass.

NOW TRY THIS!

- Write a sentence about a train.

Teachers' note Ask the children to follow the vans in the traffic jam with a finger and to read the words on them. Do these words make a sentence? Draw out that they do not make sense as a sentence because there are some words missing. They can then choose and write the missing words from the word-bank.

100% New Developing Literacy
Sentence Structure and
Punctuation: Ages 4–5
© A & C BLACK

Birthday card

100% New Developing Literacy
Sentence Structure and
Punctuation: Ages 4–5
© A & C BLACK

NOW TRY THIS!

• Make a birthday card for someone you know.

Teachers' note Ask the children to look at a birthday card and help them to read the words. What do birthday cards usually say? Ask them to write 'Happy birthday' along the clown's banner, but first ensure that they know at which side to begin. The card can then be cut out and folded so that they can address it to someone and write another message, including whom it is from, on the inside.

Get well soon

- Make a card for someone who is ill.

- Finish the flowers.
- Write on the card.

soon!

Teachers' note Ask the children to look at a get well card and help them to read the words. What do get well cards usually say? Ask them to write 'Get well' in the box, but first ensure that they know at which side to begin. The card can then be cut out and folded so that they can address it to someone and write another message, including whom it is from, on the inside.

100% New Developing Literacy
Sentence Structure and
Punctuation: Ages 4–5
© A & C BLACK

Teddy's party

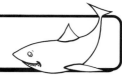

It is Teddy's birthday.

He is having a party.

• Make an invitation.

Please come to
my party on

_____ day

_____

at _____ o'clock

in Class _____ .

NOW TRY
THIS!

• **Cut out the card.**
• **On the back write**

To _____ **and** From _____

Teachers' note Provide a collection of printed party invitations for the children to read. What are invitations for? Ask the children what they need to tell the person (see Introduction). You could decide, as a group or class, on what day the party is to be, where and at what time. Each member of the group could send an invitation to someone at school.

**100% New Developing Literacy
Sentence Structure and
Punctuation: Ages 4–5
© A & C BLACK**

Don't forget!

- Finish the messages.

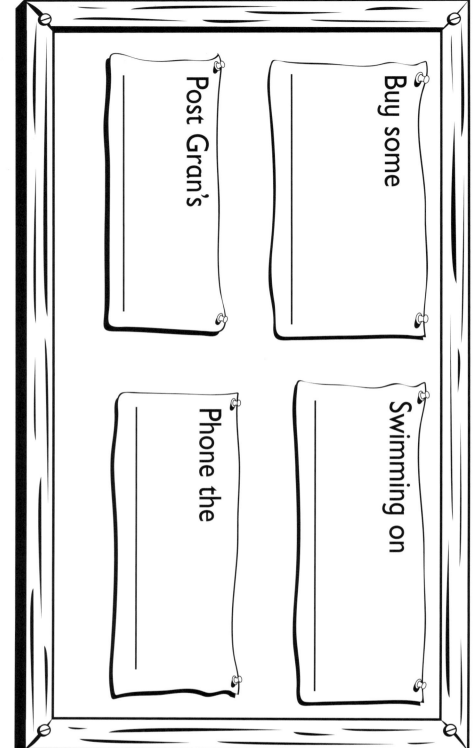

Buy some _____

Post Gran's _____

Swimming on _____

Phone the _____

Word-bank

birthday
bread
card
dentist
doctor
Friday
letter
milk
Monday
today

NOW TRY THIS!

- What must you remember?
- Write a note.

100% New Developing Literacy
Sentence Structure and
Punctuation: Ages 4–5
© A & C BLACK

Teachers' note Begin with a real memory board. Fix various messages and reminders onto it and read these with the children. Discuss what a memory board is for. Then help the children to read the words in the messages on this page. Are they sentences? Draw out that they are not because there are words missing. The children can then choose words to write in the gaps.

26

Dear Humpty Dumpty

Write a letter to Humpty Dumpty.
Tell him how to stay safe.

Dear _____

_____

_____

_____

_____

From _____

Word-bank

and	fall	not	sit
can	get	off	wall
do	hurt	safe	you

NOW TRY THIS!

- **Make an envelope for your letter.**
- **Write Humpty Dumpty on it.**

Teachers' note The children first need to have heard and recited the nursery rhyme *Humpty Dumpty*. Ask them what they would like to write to Humpty Dumpty and encourage them to use the word-bank to write sentences. They should read their sentences aloud to check that they make sense.

100% New Developing Literacy
Sentence Structure and
Punctuation: Ages 4–5
© A & C BLACK

Greetings word-bank

• Use this word-bank for spelling words on letters and cards.

Best wishes	Happy
Birthday	I would
C_____	love
Dear	New _____
Divali	par_____
Easter	to
from	_____
Get w_____	_____
Good l_____	_____
Hanukkah	_____

NOW TRY THIS!

• Write some new words in the gaps.

Use a dictionary.

Teachers' note This page can be used to support work on pages 23–25. Read the words with the children and discuss other useful words to help them to write cards and messages. They could add these as they work on the activities.

100% New Developing Literacy Sentence Structure and Punctuation: Ages 4–5 © A & C BLACK

Balloons

Fill each gap with a word from a balloon.
Read the sentence.

is   bag   has   sat   cat

Sam has a _____.

Ben _____ Jan's pal.

The dog _____ by the bin.

Mum has a _____.

Dad _____ a hat.

NOW TRY THIS!

• **Write a sentence about the picture.**

Word-bank

bed   in

is   Raj

Teachers' note Ask the children to read the first line. Is it a sentence? Draw out that it is not because there is a word missing. Help them to choose a word to write in the gap. They should then read the sentence to check that it makes sense.

100% New Developing Literacy
Sentence Structure and
Punctuation: Ages 4–5
© A & C BLACK

The bee

- **Write the missing words.**
- **Read the sentences.**

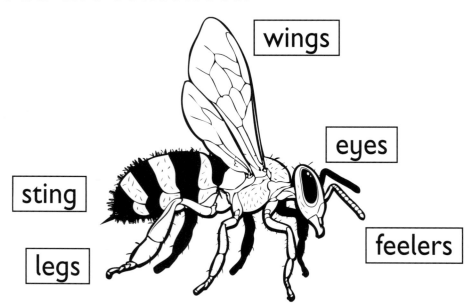

wings

eyes

sting

feelers

legs

Word-bank

bee

eyes

feelers

six

sting

two

This is a _____.

The bee has _____ wings.

It has two _____ and two _____.

It has _____ legs.

The bee can _____.

NOW TRY THIS!

- **Find out more about bees.**
- **Write the missing words.**

Bees eat _____.

They make _____.

Bees lay _____.

Look in books about bees.

Teachers' note Help the children to read the heading 'The bee' and the labels. Ask them to read the first line. Is it a sentence? Draw out that it is not because there is a word missing. Discuss how they can make these words make sense as a sentence and help them to choose a word to write in the gap. They should then read the sentence to check that it makes sense.

100% New Developing Literacy
Sentence Structure and
Punctuation: Ages 4–5
© A & C BLACK

Choose a word to fill each gap.
Colour the right flower.
Write the word.
Read the sentence.

This is a _____.

Dad has a _____.

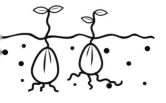

There are
two _____.

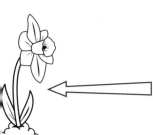

This plant has a _____.

NOW TRY THIS!

• **Write a sentence about a flower.**

Word-bank

flowers   grow
makes   sun   the

eachers' note Ask the children to read the first line. Is it a sentence? Draw out that it is not
ecause there are words missing. Discuss how they can make these words make sense as a sentence
nd help them to choose a word to write in the gap. They should then read the sentence to check
at it makes sense.

100% New Developing Literacy
Sentence Structure and
Punctuation: Ages 4–5
© A & C BLACK

Names

- **Write the names.**
- **Begin with a capital letter.**

andrew

_____

carly

_____

faria

_____

harry

_____

lee

_____

tina

_____

Aa
Bb
Cc
Dd
Ee
Ff
Gg
Hh
Ii
Jj
Kk
Ll
Mm
Nn
Oo
Pp
Qq
Rr
Ss
Tt
Uu
Vv
Ww
Xx
Yy
Zz

NOW TRY THIS!

- **Write the names of the people in your family.**

Teachers' note Point out that this page is about special words: the names of people. Explain that because they are special words they begin with a capital letter. The children could then look for the first letter of their name and its corresponding lower-case letter in the alphabet chart above. Help them to read the names and then ask them to copy them but begin with a capital letter.

100% New Developing Literacy
Sentence Structure and
Punctuation: Ages 4–5
© A & C BLACK

Name that dog

Give the dogs names.
Write on their bowls.

Names start with a capital letter.

Aa
Bb
Cc
Dd
Ee
Ff
Gg
Hh
Ii
Jj
Kk
Ll
Mm
Nn
Oo
Pp
Qq
Rr
Ss
Tt
Uu
Vv
Ww
Xx
Yy
Zz

NOW TRY THIS!

• **Write the names of your friends' pets.**

Teachers' note It is useful if the children first complete page 32. Point out that this page, too, is about special words. They are special because they are the names of dogs. Discuss the names of dogs they know and help them to think up some others. Write these up in the form of a 'Dogs' name-bank' on the board or interactive whiteboard.

100% New Developing Literacy Sentence Structure and Punctuation: Ages 4–5
© A & C BLACK

You can use I **instead of your name.**

- **Write** I **in the gaps.**
- **Read the sentences.**

____ can't fly.

____ eat fruit.

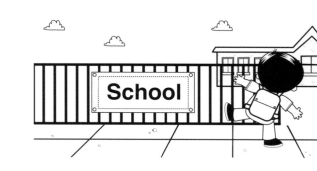

____ am not a cat.

____ go to school.

____ am not a baby.

____ read books.

NOW TRY THIS!

- **Write two more sentences with** I **.**

Teachers' note Bring a child out to the front and ask one of the others to say his or her name. Ask the others to make up a sentence about this child. Then ask the child to say it. Does it sound right? Draw out that he or she should say 'I' instead of his or her name. Point out that this is always a capital I.

100% New Developing Literacy
Sentence Structure and
Punctuation: Ages 4–5
© A & C BLACK

I see

Write your name in the gaps.
Read the sentences.

_____ can sing.

_____ likes to play.

_____ sits here.

_____ is great!

Write the sentences again.
Write $\boxed{\text{I}}$ **instead of your name.**
Read the sentences.
Circle the other words you needed to change.

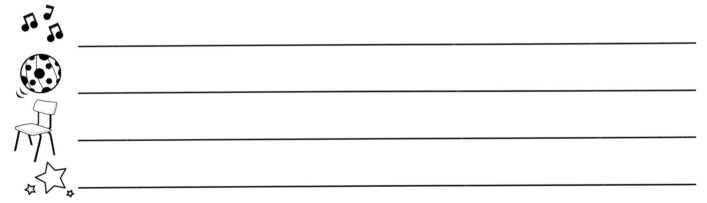

NOW TRY THIS!

- **Write two other sentences beginning with your own name.**
- **Write them again with** $\boxed{\text{I}}$ **instead of your name.**

eachers' note The children should first have completed page 34. Remind them of the sentences ey made up about someone and how that person changed the name in the sentence to 'I'.

100% New Developing Literacy
Sentence Structure and
Punctuation: Ages 4–5
© A & C BLACK

Starting off

Capital letters start a sentence.

S | <u>S</u>ix socks are in the box.

• **Write the capital letter in the gap.**

F | ___ive foxes ran away.

N | ___ine nets fell on the floor.

E | ___leven eggs broke.

O | ___ne old ox is eating grass.

 **NOW TRY THIS!**

 • **Write sentences beginning with**

A and **T**

Teachers' note Make a simple sentence of words made up of plastic or wooden letters or written on the interactive whiteboard but with the first letter of the first word missing. What is wrong with this sentence? Add the missing letter and point out that a capital letter is needed to get a sentence started. Read the sentences on this page and ask what is wrong with them.

100% New Developing Literacy
Sentence Structure and
Punctuation: Ages 4–5
© A & C BLACK

Sentences start with a capital letter.
Circle the letter which should be a capital.
Write each sentence correctly.

the old man had a red hat.

The old man had a red hat. _____

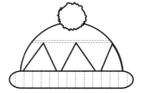

it's time for tea.

_____

you did very well.

_____

my cat is called Fluff.

_____

a rat hid under the box.

_____

hens lay eggs.

_____

NOW TRY THIS!

• **Write a sentence about a car and a sentence about a bat.**

Remember the capital letters.

Teachers' note The children should first have completed page 37. Read these sentences with them. This time there are no letters missing, but what is wrong with the sentences? The children can then write the sentences but use a capital letter to begin the first word (referring to an alphabet chart if necessary).

100% New Developing Literacy
Sentence Structure and
Punctuation: Ages 4–5
© A & C BLACK

This is a full stop: .

It is a dot.

It goes at the end of a sentence.

• Put a tick if the full stop is right. ✓

• Put a cross if it is wrong. X

 Omar ate one orange˙ 　　　X

 Ted ate two toffees.

 Theo ate three things.

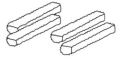 Finn ate four fish fingers.

 Fay ate five figs·

 Selina ate six sausages:

 Simon ate seven sultanas.

NOW TRY THIS!

• **Write two sentences about things you ate yesterday.**

Remember the full stops.

Teachers' note Remind the children of their work on capital letters. Emphasise that a capital letter gets a sentence started. Point out that something is needed to stop it before the next sentence, and show them how to make a full stop. They could practise drawing full stops at the right size and on the line on which they write. They can then spot the correct and incorrect full stops.

100% New Developing Literacy
Sentence Structure and
Punctuation: Ages 4–5
© A & C BLACK

Stop it!

A full stop ends a sentence.

Today we went to the zoo.

Stop.

• **Put a full stop at the end of each sentence.**

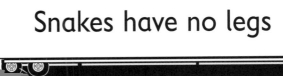

Snakes have no legs

Stop.

Stop.

The lions live in a den

Stop.

The elephants are big

Stop.

The fish live in a big tank

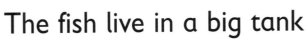 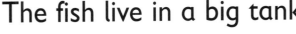 

Stop.

Crocodiles have lots of teeth

NOW TRY THIS!

• **Write two other sentences about zoo animals.**

Remember the full stops.

Teachers' note The children should first have completed page 38. Remind them that a full stop ends a sentence and remind them of the size and position of a full stop. You could read these sentences one after the other without stopping, to demonstrate what happens if there are no full stops (you don't know where to stop). They can then add the full stops to these sentences.

100% New Developing Literacy
Sentence Structure and
Punctuation: Ages 4–5
© A & C BLACK

Full stop finder: 1

- **Read the sentences.**
- **Put in the full stops.**

A sentence can go past the end of a line.

Today we are going to the park after school

Mum said that I can have some new shoes

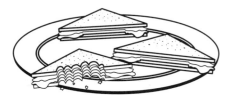

Lee and Raj came to my house for tea on Monday

It rained all day so I couldn't play in the garden

I will be five years old on my birthday

Ask your dad if you can come to my party

NOW TRY THIS!

- **Circle the wrong full stops.**

I like. red jam. I don't like blue. jam. Dad likes green jam.

Teachers' note The children should first have completed pages 36–37. Begin by reading the first sentence aloud and asking the children to point out where it ends. If they point to the end of the line, read the sentence as if there were a full stop after 'park'. Ask the children if 'after school' makes sense as a sentence. Remind them that a sentence says what is happening.

100% New Developing Literacy Sentence Structure and Punctuation: Ages 4–5 © A & C BLACK

Full stop finder: 2

- **Put in the full stops.**
- **Read the sentences.**

Check for mistakes.

We went to the shops We saw Jack and Lucy

I like fish and chips I don't like ham

A baby bear is called a cub A baby dog is a puppy

I saw Liz do a jig We saw Pip and Meg hop

NOW TRY THIS!

- **Put in the full stops.**
- **Read the sentences.**

The reds got a goal It was two goals to nil The reds will win the game

eachers' note The children should first have completed pages 38-40. Read the first example aloud without stopping for breath between the two sentences. Ask the children if this sounds right. Help hem to identify the end of the first sentence. If necessary, read other examples in this way to help he children to understand that a sentence does not always finish at the end of a line.

100% New Developing Literacy Sentence Structure and Punctuation: Ages 4–5
© A & C BLACK

41

At the seaside: 1

- **Put the words in the right order.**
- **Glue the sentences on to the sea picture.** ✂

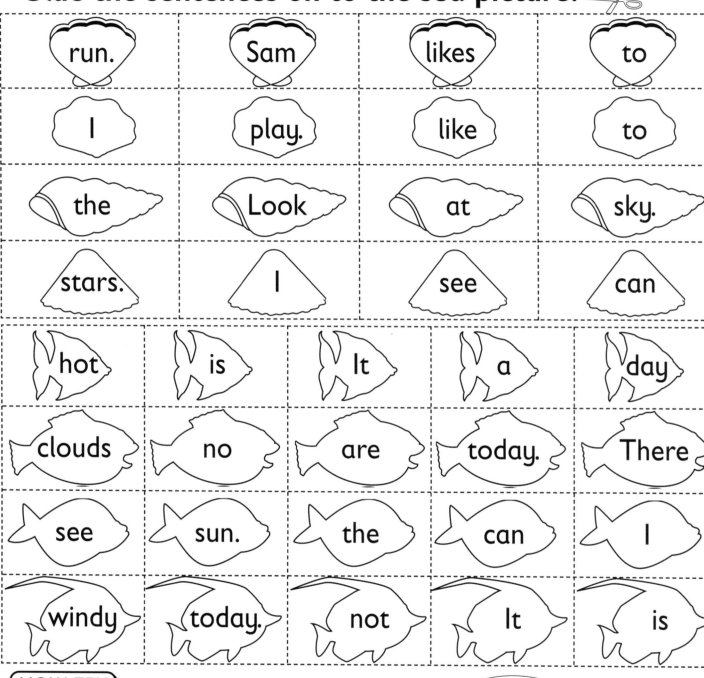

run.	Sam	likes	to
I	play.	like	to
the	Look	at	sky.
stars.	I	see	can

hot	is	It	a	day
clouds	no	are	today.	There
see	sun.	the	can	I
windy	today.	not	It	is

NOW TRY THIS!

- **Write these words in order.**

Read the sentence.

old   has   cap.   The   man   a

42

Teachers' note Ask the children to read the words on the first row of shells. Do these make sense as a sentence? Point out that they are in the wrong order. Cut them out and ask the children to try them in different orders. Once they have made a sentence they can glue the 'shells' in that order onto the beach background on page 43. They could then repeat this process for the other rows of shells and fish.

100% New Developing Literacy
Sentence Structure and
Punctuation: Ages 4–5
© A & C BLACK

At the seaside: 2

- Put the words in order.
- Glue the sentences on to the sea.

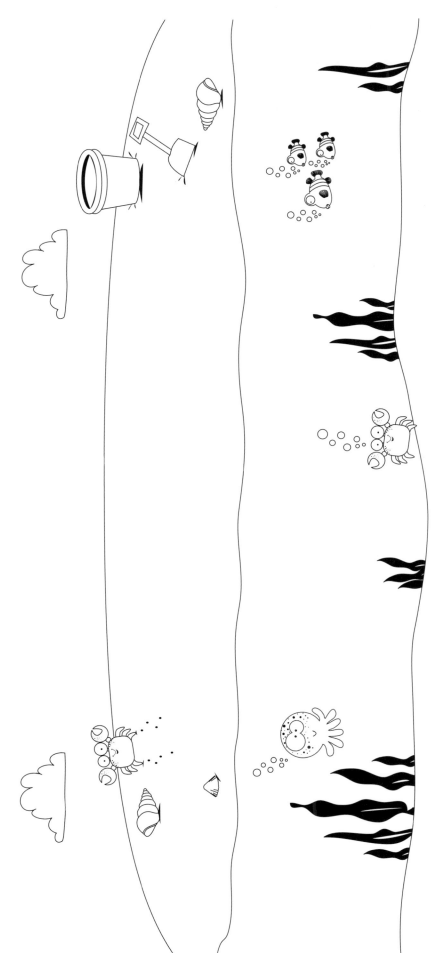

Teachers' note When you photocopy this sheet, enlarge it onto A3 paper.

Leap frogs

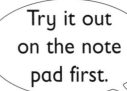

Try it out on the note pad first.

- **Read the words on the frogs.**
- **Make a sentence.**

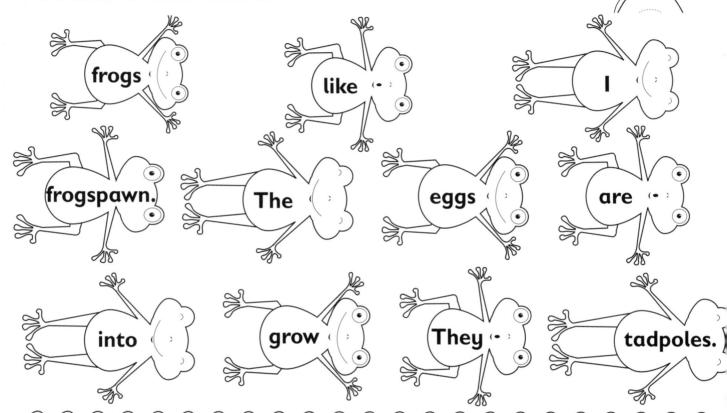

frogs   like   I

frogspawn.   The   eggs   are

into   grow   They   tadpoles.

Note pad

NOW TRY THIS!

- **Write another sentence about frogs.**
- **Use the word-bank.**

Word-bank

eggs   lay

frogs   pond   in

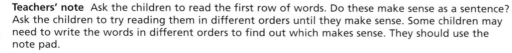

44

Teachers' note Ask the children to read the first row of words. Do these make sense as a sentence? Ask the children to try reading them in different orders until they make sense. Some children may need to write the words in different orders to find out which makes sense. They should use the note pad.

100% New Developing Literacy
Sentence Structure and
Punctuation: Ages 4–5
© A & C BLACK

Word birds

What messages are the birds bringing?
• **Write the sentences.**

rats.
I
two
see

fox
ran.
The
red

Word-bank
and   mice
eat   Owls
frogs

wings.
big
have
I

came.
big
A
yak

fish.
eat
Some
birds

2 _____

3 _____

4 _____

5 _____

NOW TRY THIS!

• **Make a sentence from the words in the word-bank.**

Teachers' note Ask the children to read the words in the first list. Can they make a sentence from
them? They might be able to recognise the first word by its capital letter and the last by the full
stop which follows it. They can then do the same with the other lists.

100% New Developing Literacy
Sentence Structure and
Punctuation: Ages 4–5
© A & C BLACK

45

Robots

The robots have mixed up the sentences.
- **Sort them out.**
- **Write the words in order.**

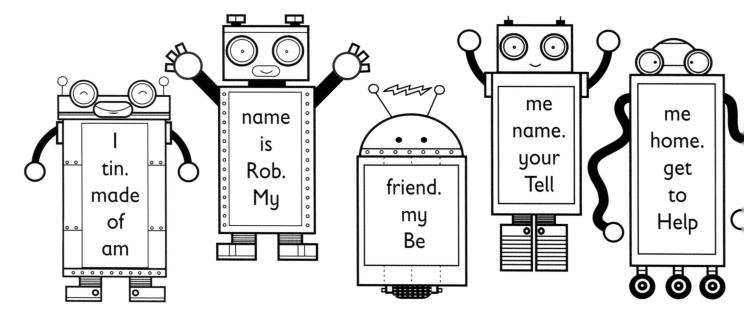

I
tin.
made
of
am

name
is
Rob.
My

friend.
my
Be

me
name.
your
Tell

me
home.
get
to
Help

1 _____

2 _____

3 _____

4 _____

5 _____

NOW TRY THIS!

- **Make a sentence from the words in the word-bank.**

Word-bank

can	robots
from	tins.
make	We

Teachers' note Ask the children to read the words in the first list. Can they make a sentence from them? They might be able to recognise the first word by its capital letter and the last by the full stop which follows it. They can then do the same with the other lists and then write each sentence.

100% New Developing Literacy
Sentence Structure and
Punctuation: Ages 4–5
© A & C BLACK

What did they do?

Write a word in each gap.

Choose words from the word-bank.

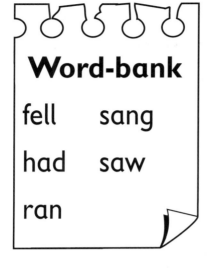

Raj _____ a cap.

May _____ fast.

I _____ a star.

Dad _____ down the steps.

Anna _____ a song.

NOW TRY THIS!

• **Write a sentence for each word.**

like   have   go

Teachers' note Read the first line of words with the children and ask them if it makes sense as a sentence. Ask them to choose a word from the word-bank to fill the gap. Draw out that the sentence now says what is going on.

100% New Developing Literacy
Sentence Structure and
Punctuation: Ages 4–5
© A & C BLACK

The big dog

- **Look at the pictures.**
- **Read the words.**
- **Join the bones to make sentences.**

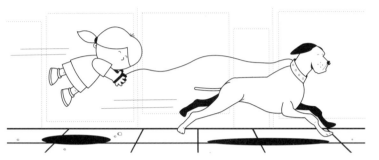

ran down the road

ate some meat

hid in a bin

played with a ball

The big dog played

in a bin.

The big dog hid

down the road.

The big dog ran

with a ball.

NOW TRY THIS!

What else did the big dog do?
- **Write a sentence.**

_____

Teachers' note Ask the children what the big dog did in each picture. Read the words with them. Ask them what the big dog played with and show them how to draw a line to join up the bones so that two sets of words make a sentence. You could use the terms 'beginning' and 'ending': 'What is the beginning of the sentence?', 'What is the ending of the sentence?'

100% New Developing Literacy
Sentence Structure and
Punctuation: Ages 4–5
© A & C BLACK

Sentence factory

Choose a word from each box.
Write a sentence.
Read the sentence.

Does it make sense?

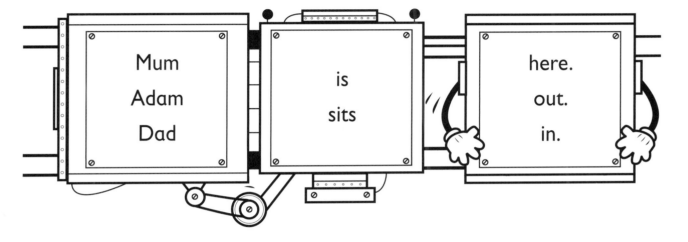

Mum		is		here.
Adam		sits		out.
Dad				in.

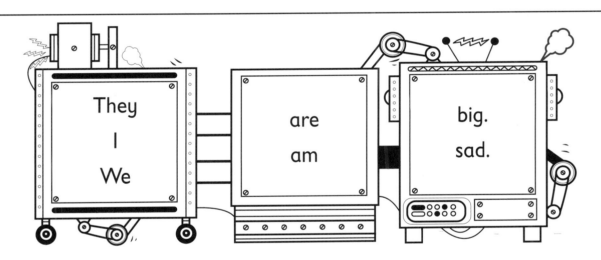

They		are		big.
I		am		sad.
We				

NOW TRY THIS!

- **Write another sentence with the words in the top machine.**
- **Write another sentence with the words in the bottom machine.**
Do your sentences make sense?

Teachers' note Help the children to make a sentence from the first 'machine' by choosing a word from each part of it. Ask them to write the sentence on the line below the machine. They can then do the same with the second machine and, in the extension activity, make a different sentence from the words in each machine.

100% New Developing Literacy
Sentence Structure and
Punctuation: Ages 4–5
© A & C BLACK

Silly sentences

- Use the word-banks to make silly sentences.
- Write your sentences on a new piece of paper.

Word-bank

Curly

Grandad

Mum

Ella

Leo

Tibby

Word-bank

ate

bit   saw

cooked

found

hid

hit

hugged

lost

made

painted

patted

Word-bank

a bag   a rock

a cake   a tree

a doll   a van

a fan   a yam

a hat

a jug

a lolly

a mop

a pen

a rat

Teachers' note This is a game of 'consequences'. Ask the children to work in groups of three. Use the word-banks for reference and give each child a blank strip of paper. Each child writes a name from the first word-bank at the top of the strip, folds it under and passes it to the next player, who writes a word from the second column, etc. Once finished, the strips can be opened and the resulting sentences read aloud.

100% New Developing Literacy
Sentence Structure and
Punctuation: Ages 4–5
© A & C BLACK

The park

Look at the picture.
What can you see?
Write the missing words.

slide

swing

football

bike

bat

dog

can see a _____ .

can see _____ .

can _____ .

_____ .

NOW TRY THIS!

- **Draw a picture of your playground.**
- **Write a sentence about it.**

eachers' note Ask the children what the picture shows and what they can see in the park. Help hem to complete the first sentence. They can then complete the sentences using this as a model nd the labels to help them to spell the words. Draw out that they have written a caption which a sentence.

100% New Developing Literacy
Sentence Structure and
Punctuation: Ages 4–5
© A & C BLACK

Zoo time

What is at the zoo?
- **Write the missing words.**

giraffe

elephant

monkey

hippo

lion

tiger

At the zoo there is a _____

At the zoo there is _____

At the zoo there _____

At the zoo _____

At the _____

_____

NOW TRY THIS!

What else could there be at the zoo?
- **Write two sentences.**

Teachers' note Ask the children what the picture shows and what they can see in the zoo. Help them to complete the first sentence. They can then complete the sentences using this as a model and the labels to help them to spell the words. Draw out that they have written a caption which is a sentence.

100% New Developing Literacy
Sentence Structure and
Punctuation: Ages 4–5
© A & C BLACK

In the street

What is there in the street?
• Write the missing words.

There is a shop in the street.

There is a _____ in the street.

_____ in the street.

_____ .

_____ .

_____ .

_____ .

NOW TRY THIS!

• Draw your street.
• Write two sentences about it.

Teachers' note Ask the children what the picture shows and what they can see in the street. Help them to complete the first sentence. They can then complete the sentences using this as a model and the labels to help them to spell the words. Draw out that they have written a caption which is a sentence.

100% New Developing Literacy
Sentence Structure and
Punctuation: Ages 4–5
© A & C BLACK

53

On the beach

- **What can you find on the beach?**
- **Write the missing words.**

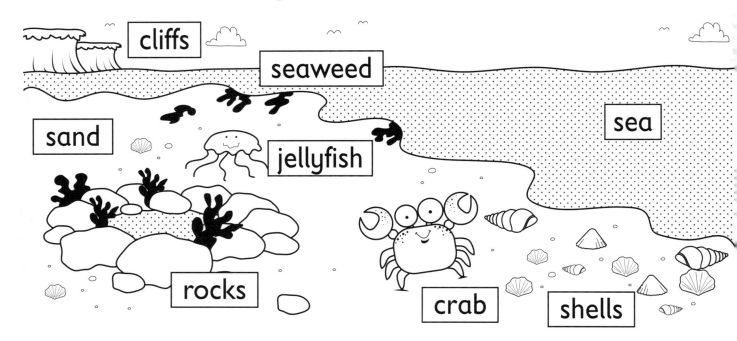

cliffs

seaweed

sea

sand

jellyfish

rocks

crab

shells

I can find sand on the beach.

I can find _____ on the beach.

I can find _____ on _____.

I can _____.

_____.

_____.

_____.

NOW TRY THIS!

What have you found on the beach?
- **Write two sentences.**

Teachers' note Ask the children what the picture shows and what they can see on the beach. Help them to complete the first sentence. They can then complete the sentences using this as a model and the labels to help them to spell the words. Draw out that they have written a caption which is a sentence.

**100% New Developing Literacy
Sentence Structure and
Punctuation: Ages 4–5**
© A & C BLACK

Treasure hunt

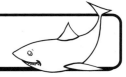

- **Follow the treasure hunt.**
- **Finish the sentences.**

I found a bag.

Then I found a _____.

Then I found a _____.

Then I found a _____.

Then I found a _____.

NOW TRY THIS!

- **Make a treasure hunt for a friend.**
- **Write what your friend finds.**

Teachers' note Help the children to follow the trail of the treasure hunt. Point out the first sentence and then continue along the trail, saying, 'Then I found a …' (ask the children to supply the missing word). Continue to the end. Then let the children repeat this with a partner and write the sentences, using the first one as a model and the captions to help them to spell the words.

100% New Developing Literacy
Sentence Structure and
Punctuation: Ages 4–5
© A & C BLACK

Follow my leader

Look at the pictures of Sooty.
• Finish the sentences.

Sooty walks.

Then Sooty _____.

Then Sooty _____.

Then _____.

Then _____.

_____.

NOW TRY THIS!

• **Play follow my leader with a friend.**
• **Draw what you do.**
• **Write sentences about it.**

Teachers' note Help the children to follow Sooty's walk, saying, 'Sooty walks.' Point out the first sentence and then continue, saying, 'Then Sooty …' (ask the children to supply the missing word). Continue to the last caption and then let the children repeat this with a partner and write the sentences, using the first one as a model and the captions to help them to spell the words.

100% New Developing Literacy Sentence Structure and Punctuation: Ages 4–5
© A & C BLACK

Route cards: 1

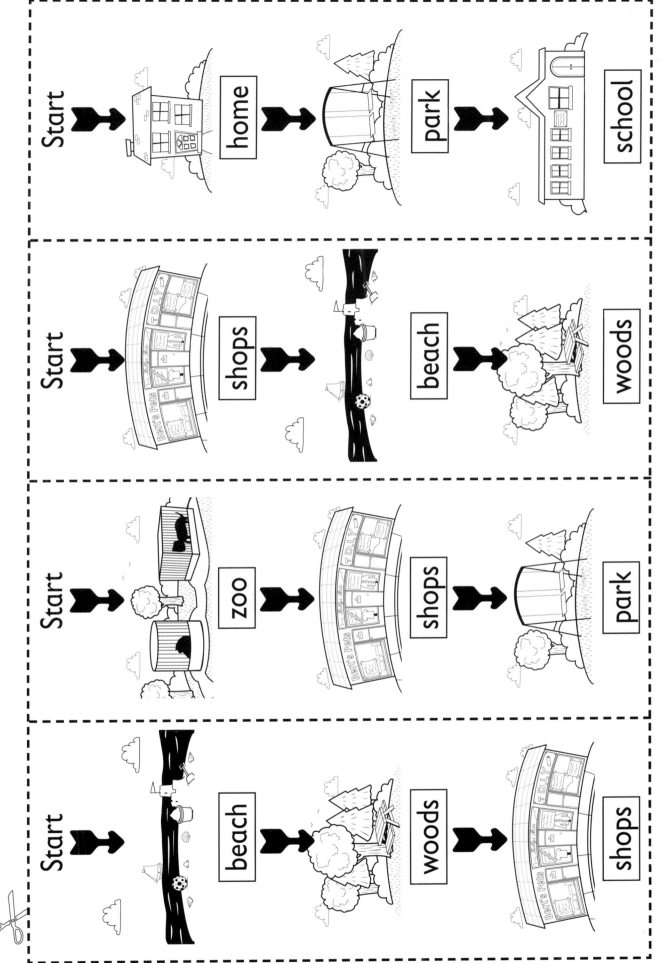

Start ➤ home ➤ park ➤ school

Start ➤ shops ➤ beach ➤ woods

Start ➤ zoo ➤ shops ➤ park

Start ➤ beach ➤ woods ➤ shops

Teachers' note Cut out the route cards and give the children one each. Invite a child to follow the route with a finger and to say what he or she passes on the route. Help him or her to express this in sentences: 'I went to the shops. Then I went to the woods. Then I went to the beach.' The children can continue in this way in groups and then write their sentences (see page 58).

100% New Developing Literacy Sentence Structure and Punctuation: Ages 4–5
© A & C BLACK

- **Take turns to choose a route card.**
- **Tell a friend about your route.**
- **Write sentences about it.**

I went to the _____

Then I went to the _____

Then I went _____

I went to the _____

Then I went to _____

Then _____

I went to _____

Then I went _____

Then _____

I went _____

Then _____

_____

NOW TRY THIS!

- **Make a route card about places you go to.**
- **Write sentences about it.**

Teachers' note This provides a format to help the children to write sentences about the route cards on page 57. They could also make up route cards about routes around the classroom and then write sentences about them.

100% New Developing Literacy
Sentence Structure and
Punctuation: Ages 4–5
© A & C BLACK

Along the street: 1

Four can play.

- **Roll a dice.**
- **Move your counter.**
- **Pick up a card.**

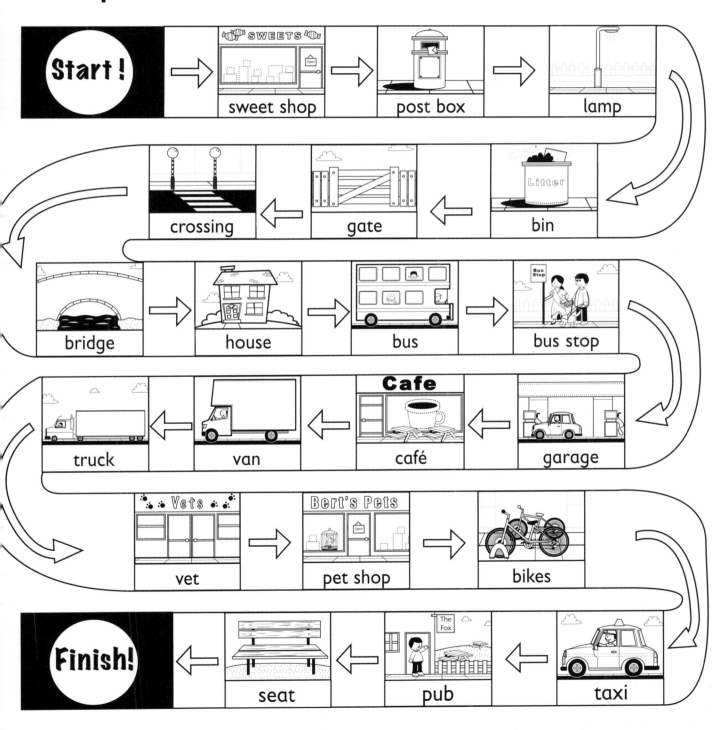

Teachers' note Four children can play this dice game. They take turns to roll a dice. They pick up a card (see page 60) according to the items they land on. If they land on an item where the card has already been taken, they move to the next item. Continued on page 60.

100% New Developing Literacy Sentence Structure and Punctuation: Ages 4–5
© A & C BLACK

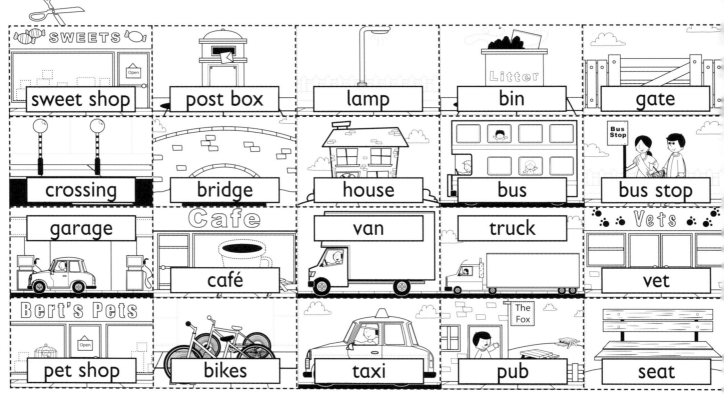

sweet shop	post box	lamp	bin	gate
crossing	bridge	house	bus	bus stop
garage / café	van	truck		vet
pet shop	bikes	taxi	pub	seat

• **Look at your cards.**

• **Write sentences about them.**

Along the street I saw a _____

Then I saw _____

Then I saw _____

Then _____

Then _____

Then _____

NOW TRY THIS!

• **Write about a walk along a street you know.**

Teachers' note This supports the game on page 59. Once the last player has moved off the board the children should arrange their cards in order. They can then glue them on to a route card and describe the route in sentences, which they could then write, using the format on this page to help them.

100% New Developing Literacy
Sentence Structure and
Punctuation: Ages 4–5
© A & C BLACK

I can tap, tap, tap

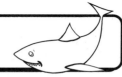

Help Teddy to make up a song.
- **Do the actions.**
- **Write the words.**

I can _____, _____, _____.

tap

I can _____, _____, _____.

clap

I can _____, _____, _____.

stamp

I can _____, _____, _____.

click

NOW TRY THIS!

What else could Teddy sing?
- **Do the actions.**
- **Sing the song.**
- **Write the words.**

Teachers' note Begin by singing 'I can tap, tap, tap' and tapping your hand on a table top. Repeat this and ask the children to join in. Ask them to look at the next picture and caption and to sing the sentence, and so on. They can then write the missing words.

100% New Developing Literacy
Sentence Structure and
Punctuation: Ages 4–5
© A & C BLACK

Old Macdonald's farm

- **What did Old Macdonald have?**
- **Finish the sentences.**

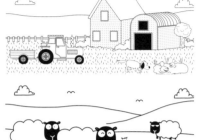

Old Macdonald had a _____ .

Old Macdonald had a _____ _____
on that farm he had some _____ .

Old Macdonald had a _____ _____
on that _____ he had some
_____ .

Old Macdonald had a _____ _____
on that _____ he had
_____ _____ .

Old Macdonald had a _____ _____
on that _____ he had some
_____ .

NOW TRY THIS!

What else did Old Macdonald have?
- **Sing the song.**
- **Write a sentence.**

Teachers' note Sing the song *Old Macdonald Had a Farm* with the children and then ask them to read the first line. Does it make sense as a sentence? Ask them to supply the missing word and to write it, using the caption to help them to spell it.

100% New Developing Literacy Sentence Structure and Punctuation: Ages 4–5
© A & C BLACK

Mrs Snip

- **Make up a song about Mrs Snip.**
- **Finish the sentence.**
- **Write the words.**

Mrs Snip _____ my hair.

Splash, splash, splash.

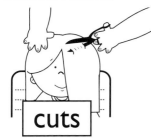

Mrs Snip _____ my _____.

Snip, _____, _____.

Mrs Snip _____ my hair.

Blow, _____, _____.

Mrs Snip _____ my _____.

Comb, _____, _____.

NOW TRY THIS!

What else could Mrs Snip do?
- **Write a sentence.**
- **Write the words.**

Teachers' note Sing the first line with the children, stopping for them to supply the missing word. (You could sing it to the tune of *Old Macdonald Had a Farm*.) Once they have sung the entire song the children can write the missing words.

100% New Developing Literacy
Sentence Structure and
Punctuation: Ages 4–5
© A & C BLACK

Goldilocks

• **Finish the sentences.**

hot

This is too _____.

big

This is too _____.

small

This is _____.

cold

_____.

NOW TRY THIS!

• **Write two other sentences for Goldilocks.**

• **Use the word-bank.**

Word-bank
hard
soft

Teachers' note Ask the children what they know about Goldilocks. What did she do? What did she say? Tell them they are going to read some things Goldilocks said. Invite them to supply the missing words.

100% New Developing Literacy
Sentence Structure and
Punctuation: Ages 4–5
© A & C BLACK